Name ______________________

HUNDRED CHART

1	2	3	4	5	6	7	8	9	10
11	12	13	14	15	16	17	18	19	20
21	22	23	24	25	26	27	28	29	30
31	32	33	34	35	36	37	38	39	40
41	42	43	44	45	46	47	48	49	50
51	52	53	54	55	56	57	58	59	60
61	62	63	64	65	66	67	68	69	70
71	72	73	74	75	76	77	78	79	80
81	82	83	84	85	86	87	88	89	90
91	92	93	94	95	96	97	98	99	100

Name

SPINNER BLANKS, SHEET 1

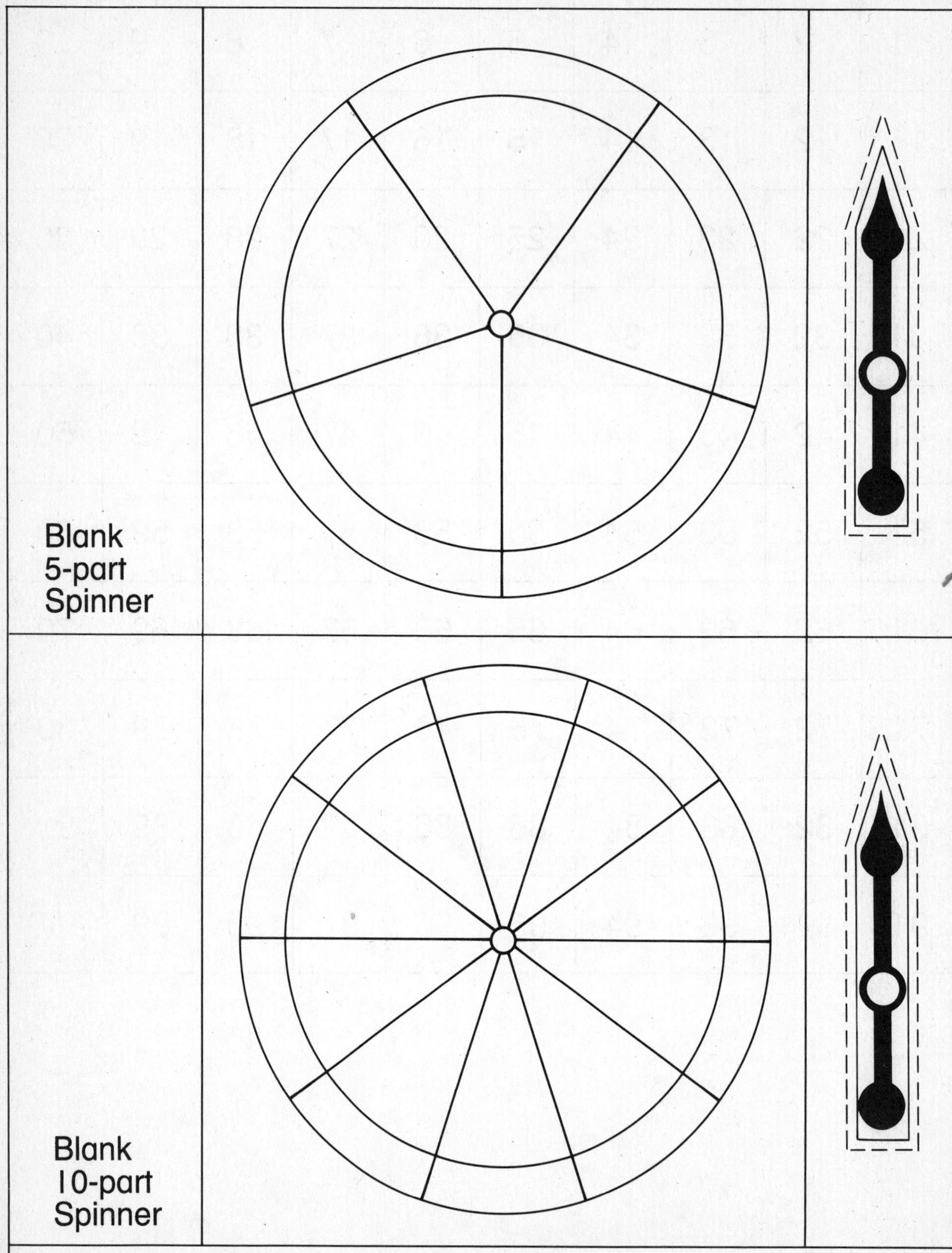

1. Complete the spinner.
2. Add color.
3. Mount on heavy paper.
4. Cut out and punch holes.
5. Attach spinner with a paper fastener.

Name

SPINNER BLANKS, SHEET 2

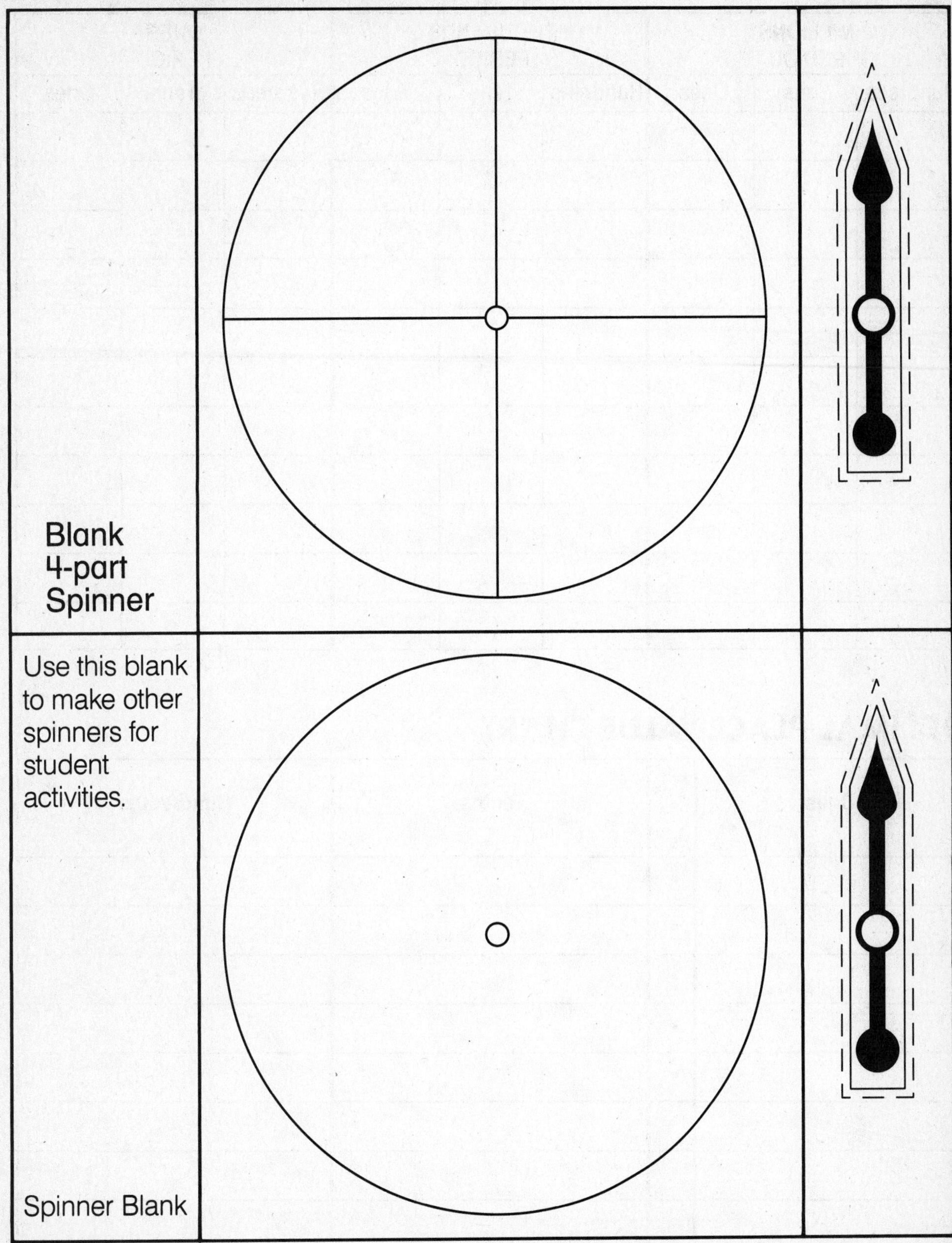

Blank
4-part
Spinner

Use this blank to make other spinners for student activities.

Spinner Blank

1. Complete the spinner.
2. Add color.
3. Mount on heavy paper.
4. Cut out and punch holes.
5. Attach spinner with a paper fastener.

Name ______________________________

PLACE-VALUE CHART (MILLIONS)

MILLIONS PERIOD			THOUSANDS PERIOD			ONES PERIOD		
Hundreds	Tens	Ones	Hundreds	Tens	Ones	Hundreds	Tens	Ones

DECIMAL PLACE-VALUE CHART

Ones	•	Tenths	Hundredths
	•		
	•		
	•		
	•		
	•		
	•		
	•		
	•		
	•		
	•		
	•		

Name

PLACE-VALUE MAT

Name

ADDITION/MULTIPLICATION FACT CHART

	0	1	2	3	4	5	6	7	8	9
0										
1										
2										
3										
4										
5										
6										
7										
8										
9										

Name

CENTIMETER GRAPH PAPER

Name

INCH GRAPH PAPER

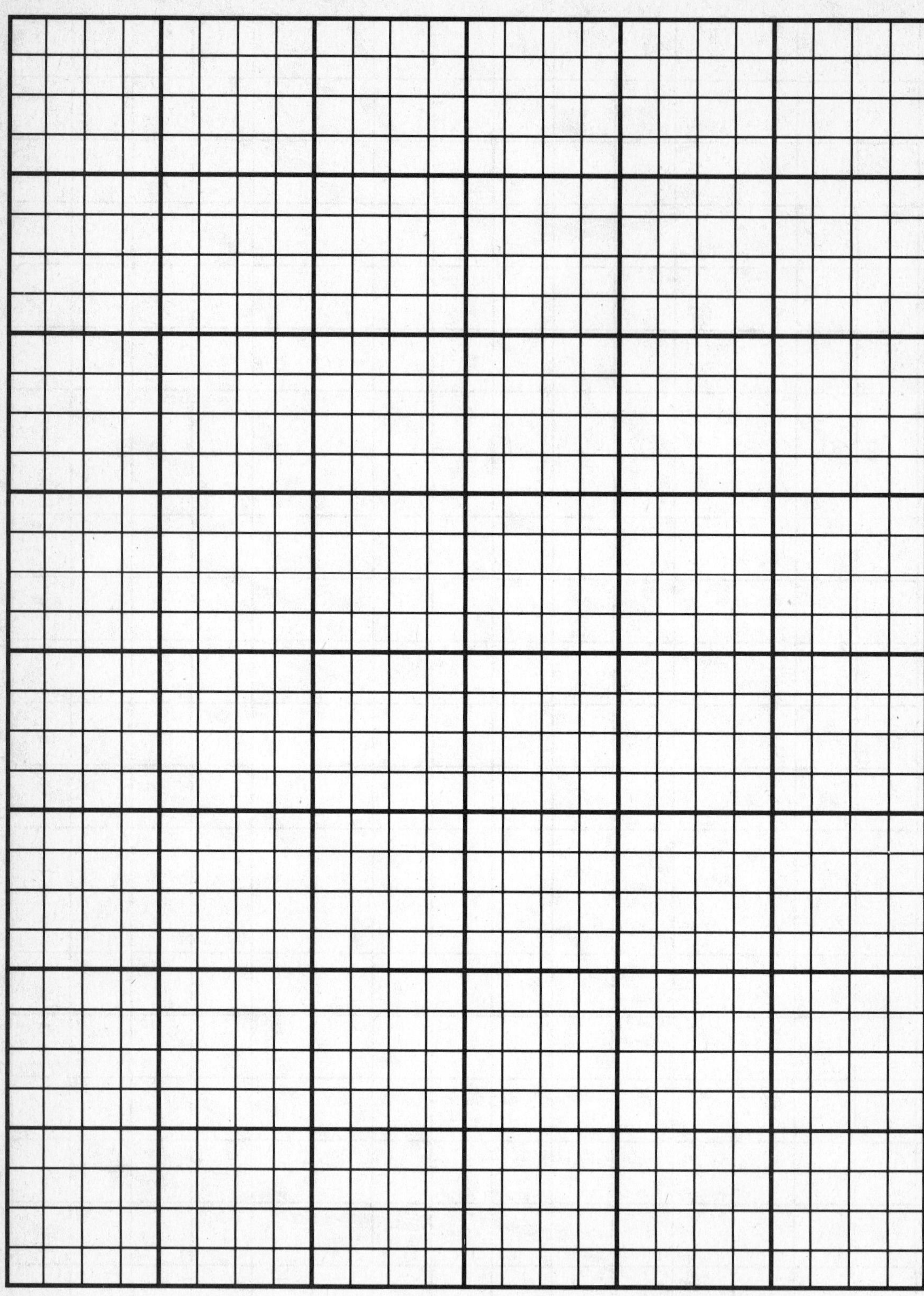

Name ______________________________

CENTIMETER DOT PAPER

Coins

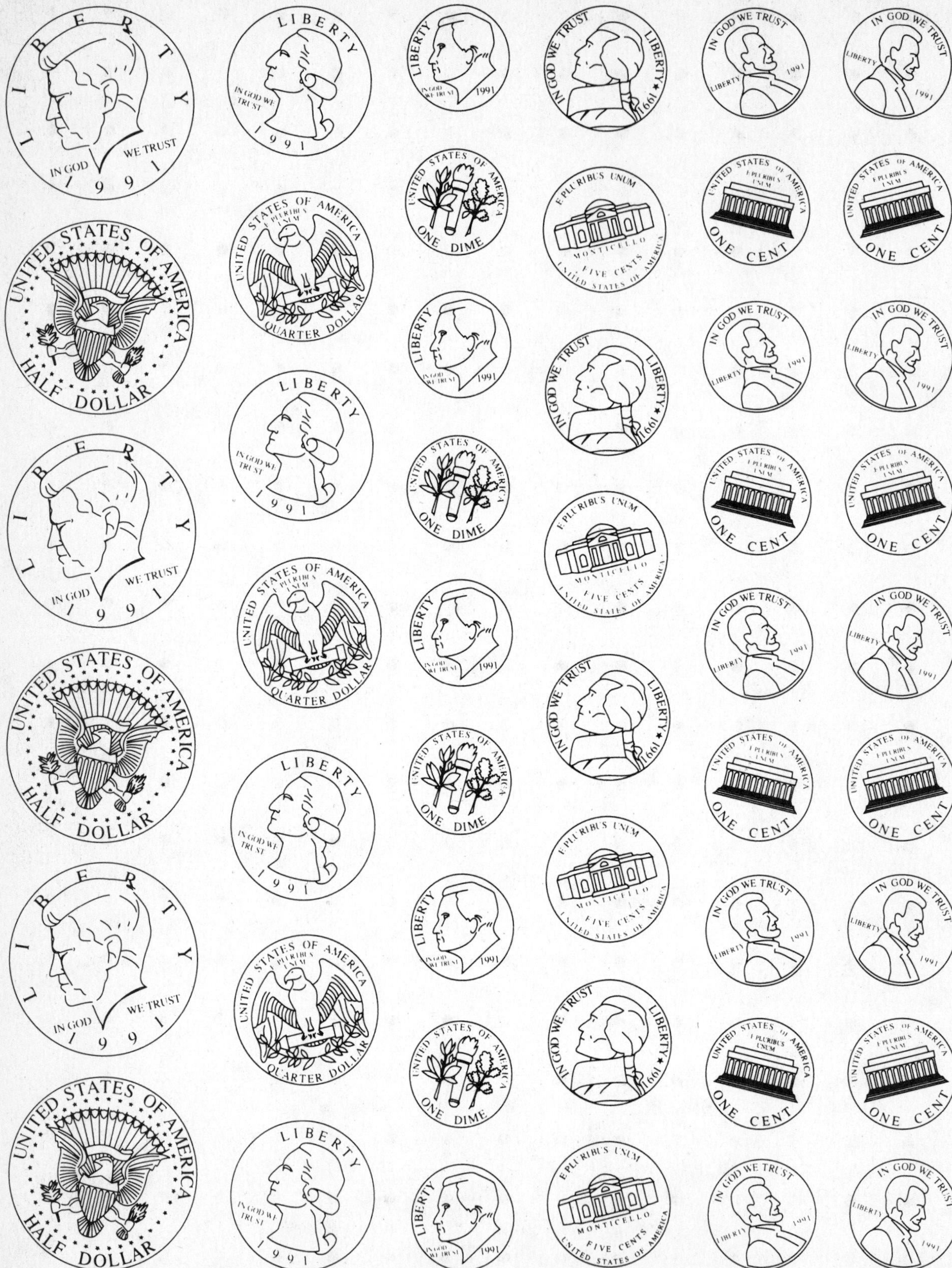
LIBERTY
IN GOD WE TRUST
1991
UNITED STATES OF AMERICA
HALF DOLLAR
E PLURIBUS UNUM
QUARTER DOLLAR
ONE DIME
MONTICELLO
FIVE CENTS
ONE CENT

Name

BILLS

NOT LEGAL TENDER
THE UNITED STATES OF AMERICA
SCHOOL MONEY
ONE
LR
ONE DOLLAR

LEARNING RESOURCES MONEY
PLAY MONEY
ONE
ONE DOLLAR

NOT LEGAL TENDER
THE UNITED STATES OF AMERICA
SCHOOL MONEY
FIVE
LR
FIVE DOLLARS

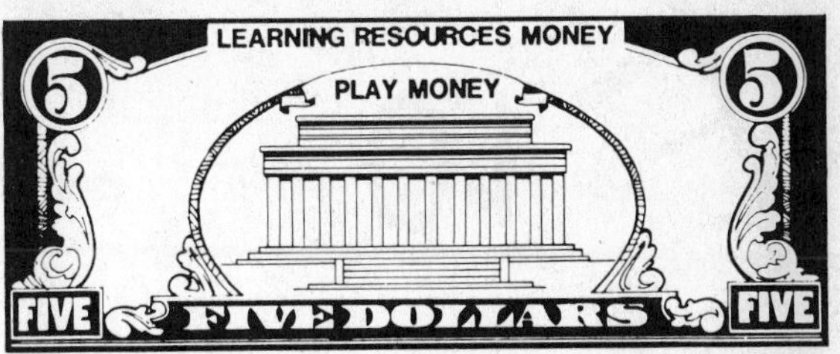
LEARNING RESOURCES MONEY
PLAY MONEY
FIVE
FIVE DOLLARS
FIVE

NOT LEGAL TENDER
THE UNITED STATES OF AMERICA
SCHOOL MONEY
TEN
LR
TEN DOLLARS

LEARNING RESOURCES MONEY
PLAY MONEY
TEN DOLLARS

NOT LEGAL TENDER
THE UNITED STATES OF AMERICA
SCHOOL MONEY
TWENTY
LR
TWENTY DOLLARS

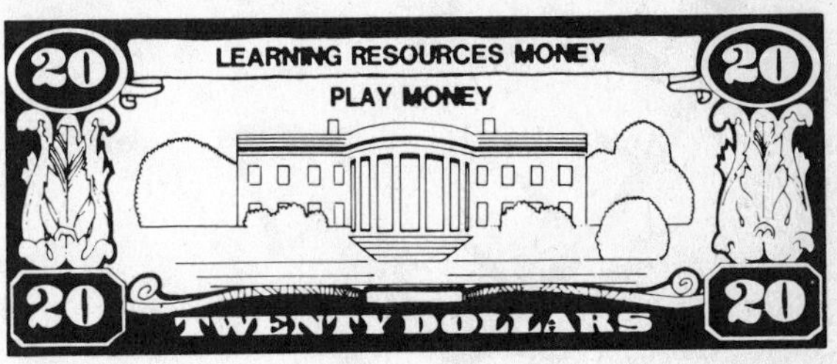
LEARNING RESOURCES MONEY
PLAY MONEY
TWENTY DOLLARS

NOT LEGAL TENDER
SCHOOL MONEY
FIFTY
LR
THE
UNITED STATES OF AMERICA
FIFTY DOLLARS

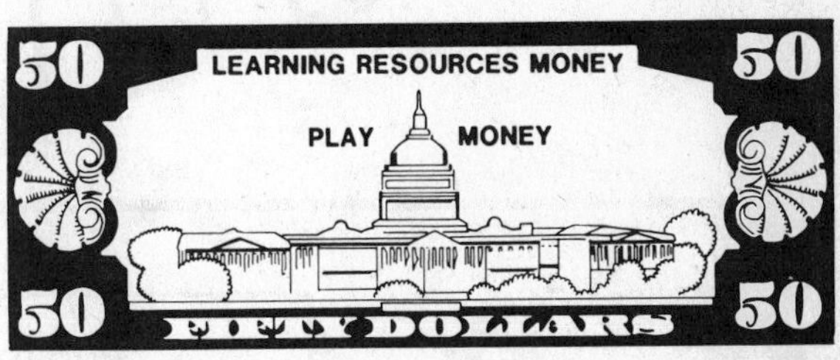
LEARNING RESOURCES MONEY
PLAY
MONEY
FIFTY DOLLARS

NOT LEGAL TENDER
THE UNITED STATES OF AMERICA
SCHOOL MONEY
100
LR
ONE HUNDRED DOLLARS

LEARNING RESOURCES MONEY
PLAY
MONEY
ONE HUNDRED DOLLARS

Name ____________________

ANALOG CLOCK

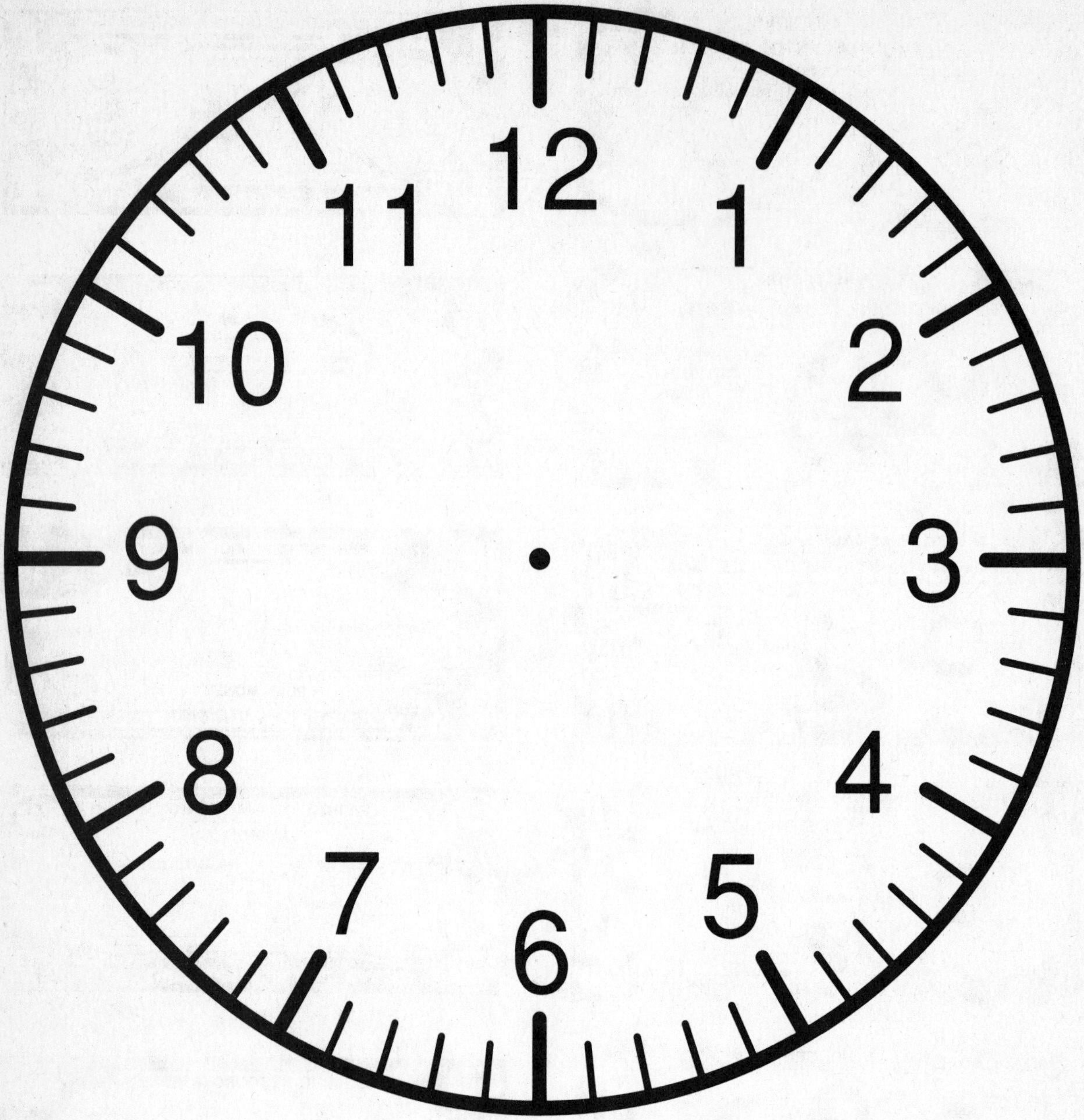

12
11
1
10
2
9
3
8
4
7
5
6

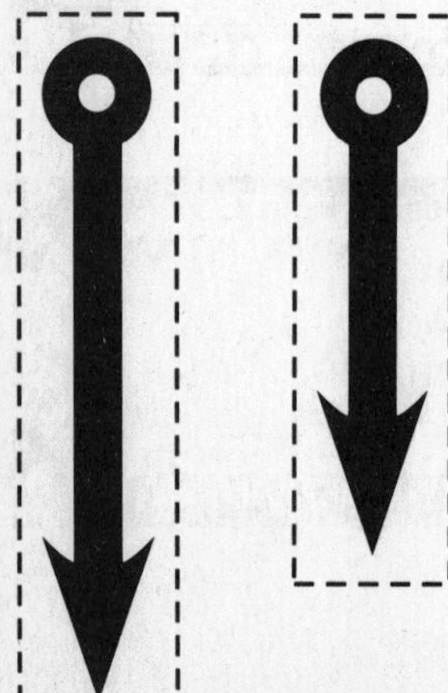

1. Glue the clock face on heavy paper.
2. Cut out the clock hands.
3. Attach them to the clock with a paper fastener.

Name

TWO-COLOR COUNTERS

Name ________________________________

NUMBER LINES

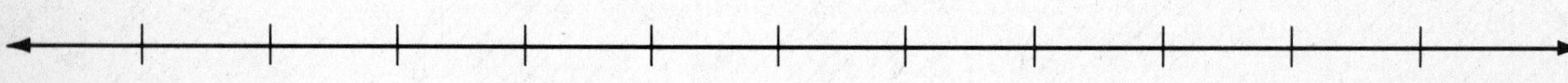

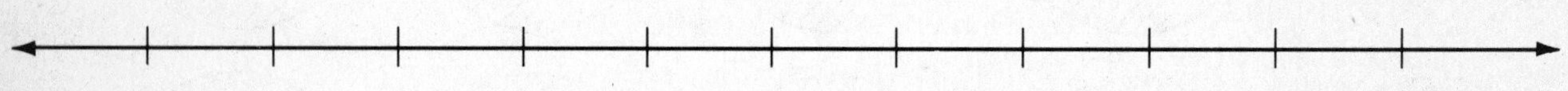

Name

GEOBOARD

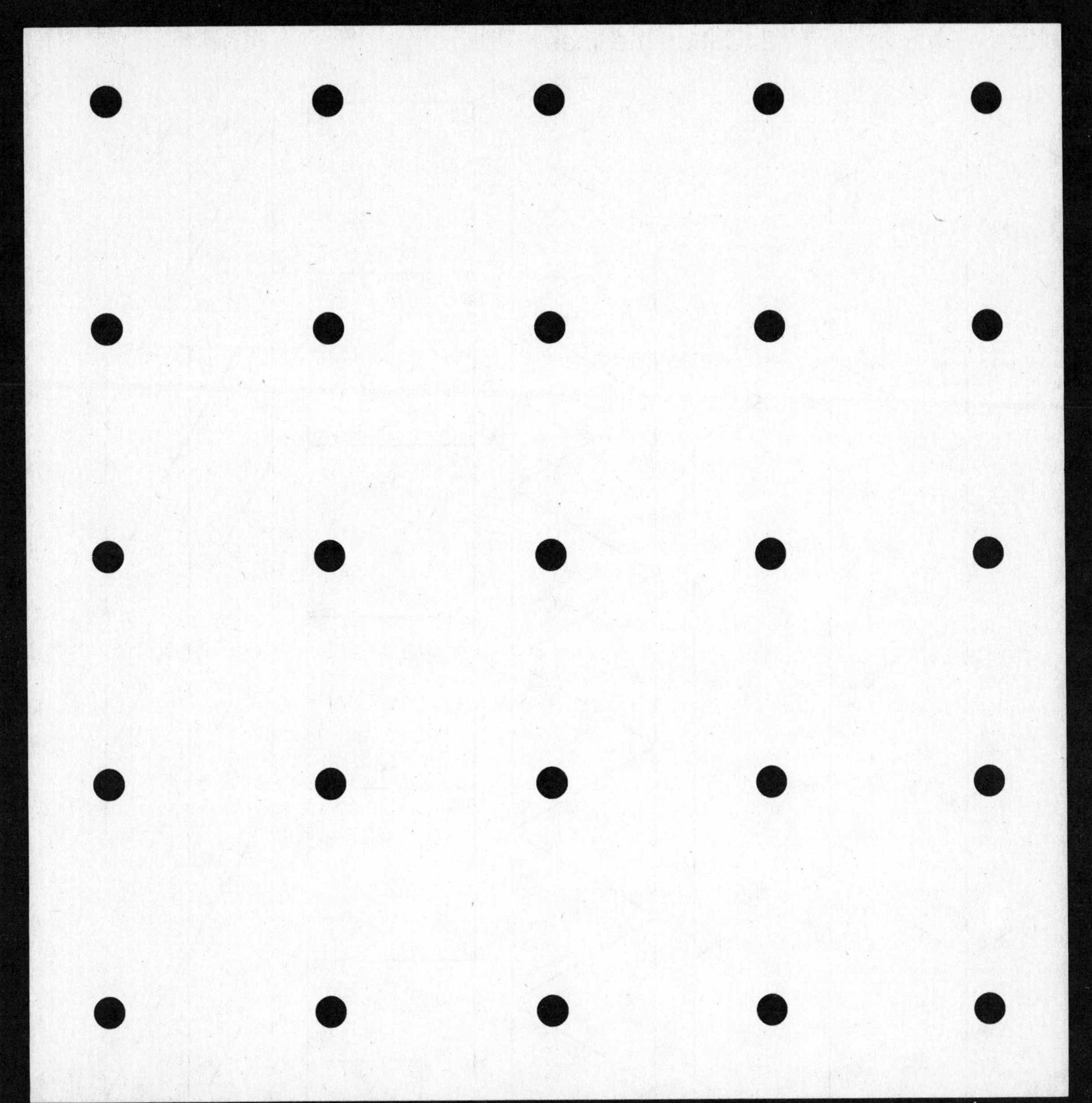

Name

PATTERN BLOCKS, SHEET 1

1. Color the shapes. 2. Cut on the lines.

Red Green Orange Tan

Name

PATTERN BLOCKS, SHEET 2

1. Color the shapes. 2. Cut on the lines.

Name ______________________

RULERS: INCH, CENTIMETER

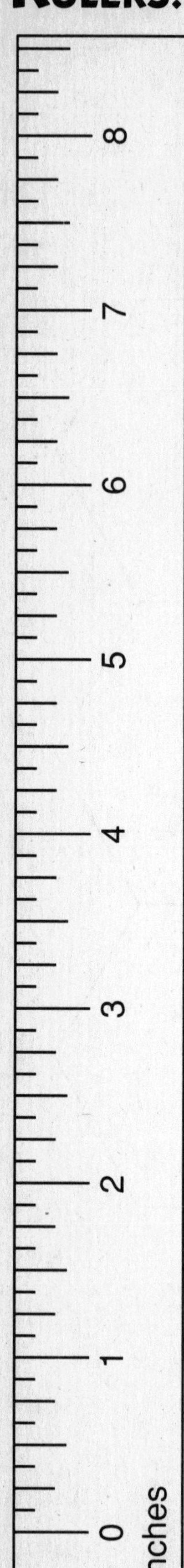

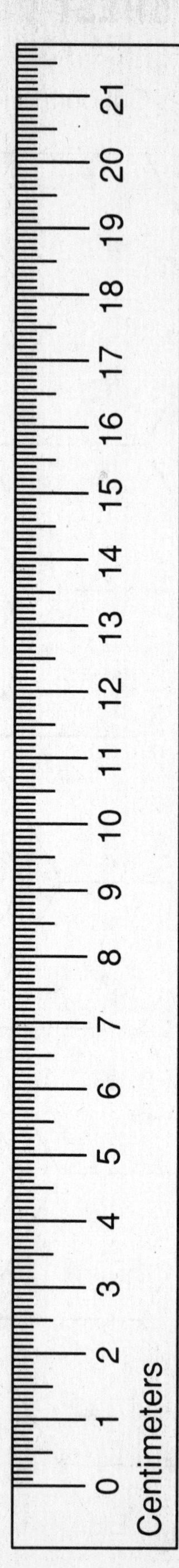

Name ______________________________

CUSTOMARY MEASURING TAPE (1 YARD)

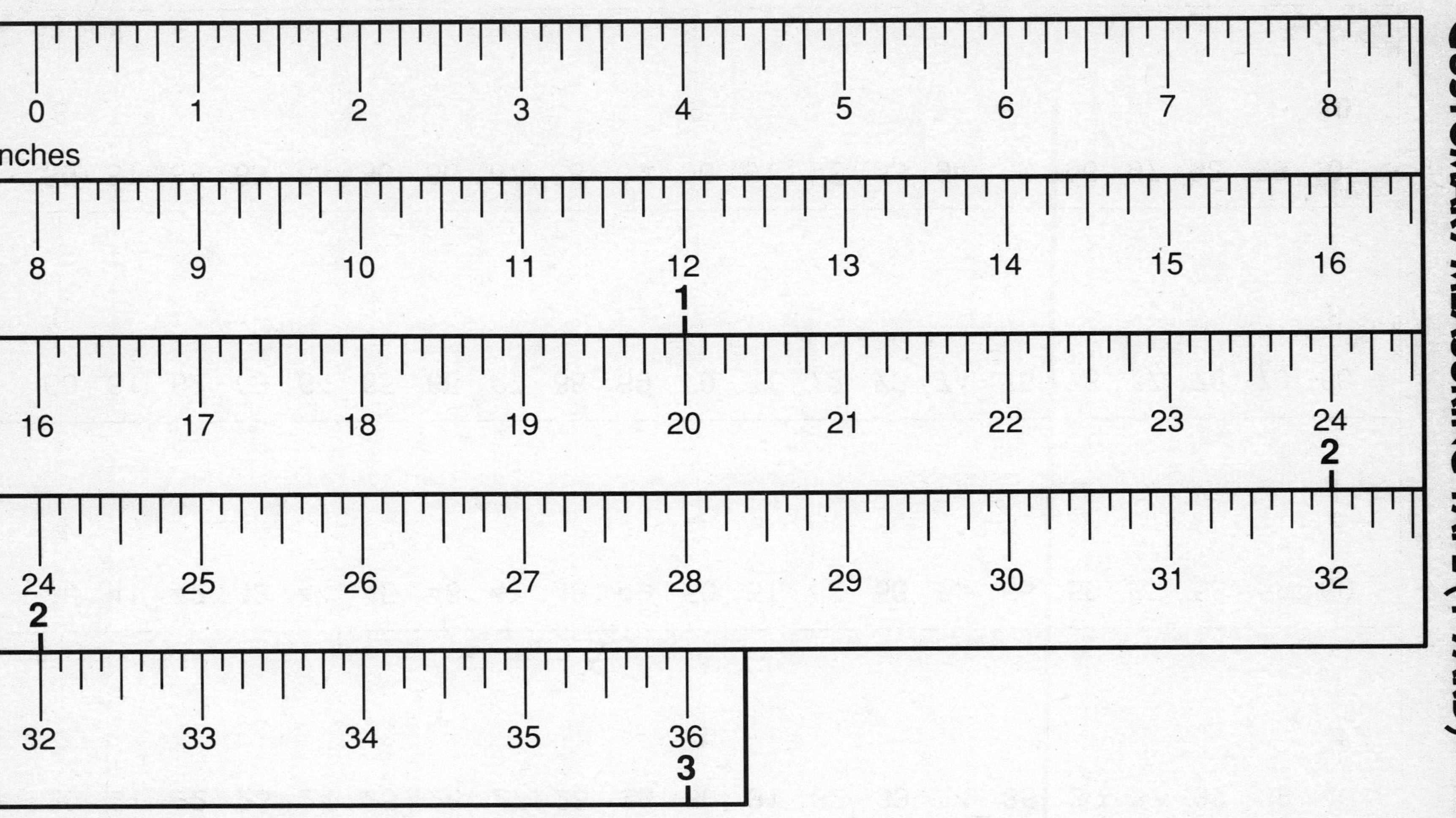

To make a yardstick of 36 inches:
1. Cut out all of the strips.
2. Carefully overlap each strip.
3. Tape or glue them together to form a yardstick.

Name ______________________

METRIC MEASURING TAPE (1 METER)

centimeters 0 1 2 3 4 5 6 7 8 9 10 11 12 13 14 15 16 17 18 19 20
decimeters 0 1 2

20 21 22 23 24 25 26 27 28 29 30 31 32 33 34 35 36 37 38 39 40
2 3 4

40 41 42 43 44 45 46 47 48 49 50 51 52 53 54 55 56 57 58 59 60
4 5 6

60 61 62 63 64 65 66 67 68 69 70 71 72 73 74 75 76 77 78 79 80
6 7 8

80 81 82 83 84 85 86 87 88 89 90 91 92 93 94 95 96 97 98 99 100
8 9 10

Cut strips apart. Tape them together for a metric measuring tape.

Name ______________________________

TANGRAM SHAPES

1. Cut on the lines.
2. Use the shapes to form a picture or a pattern.
3. You may wish to color the shapes before cutting.

Name

PLACE-VALUE MODELS

Ones

Tens

Hundreds

1	2	3	4	5	6	7	8	9	10
11	12	13	14	15	16	17	18	19	20
21	22	23	24	25	26	27	28	29	30
31	32	33	34	35	36	37	38	39	40
41	42	43	44	45	46	47	48	49	50
51	52	53	54	55	56	57	58	59	60
61	62	63	64	65	66	67	68	69	70
71	72	73	74	75	76	77	78	79	80
81	82	83	84	85	86	87	88	89	90
91	92	93	94	95	96	97	98	99	100

Name ______________________

SOLID GEOMETRIC FIGURE PATTERNS
SHEET 1

1. Cut on solid lines.
2. Fold on dashed lines.
3. Tape or glue to form solid shapes.

Cube

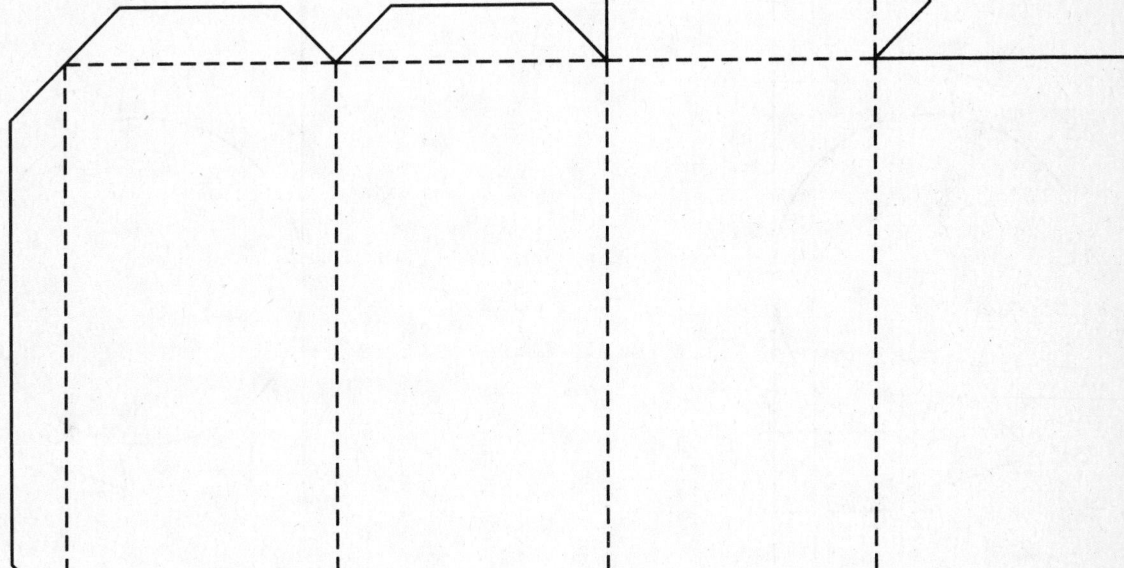

Rectangular Prism

Name

SOLID GEOMETRIC FIGURE PATTERNS
SHEET 2

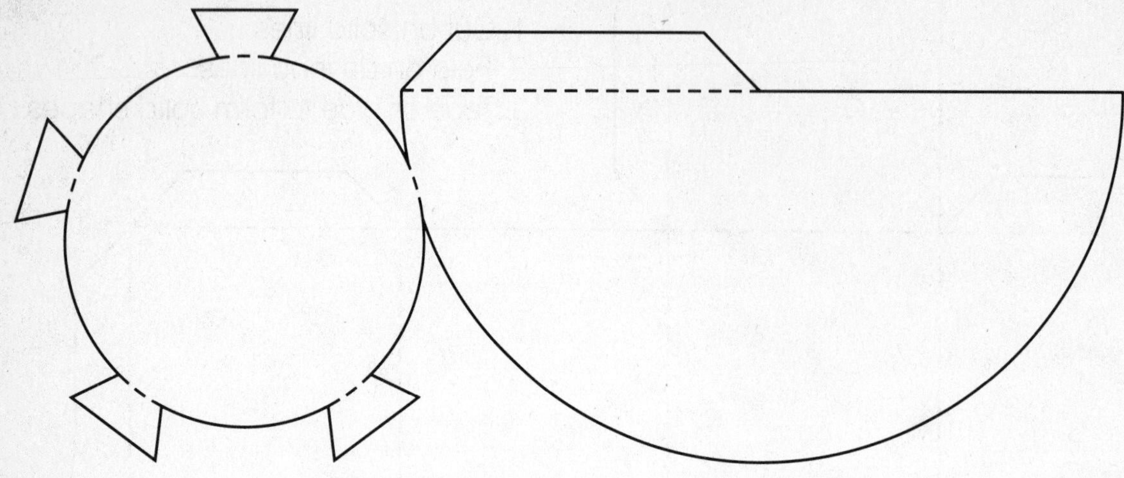

Cone

1. Cut on solid lines.
2. Fold on dashed lines.
3. Tape or glue to form solid shapes.

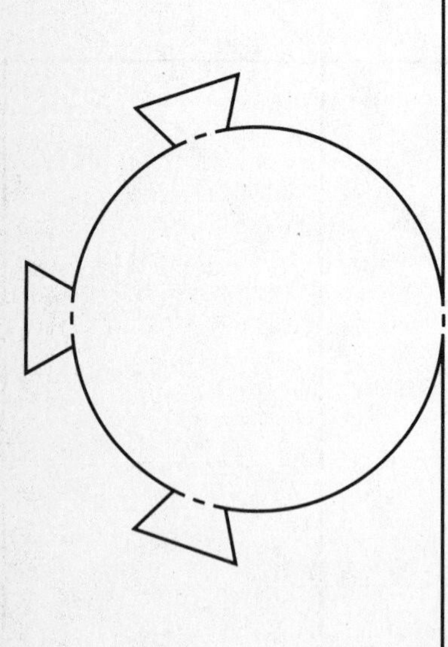

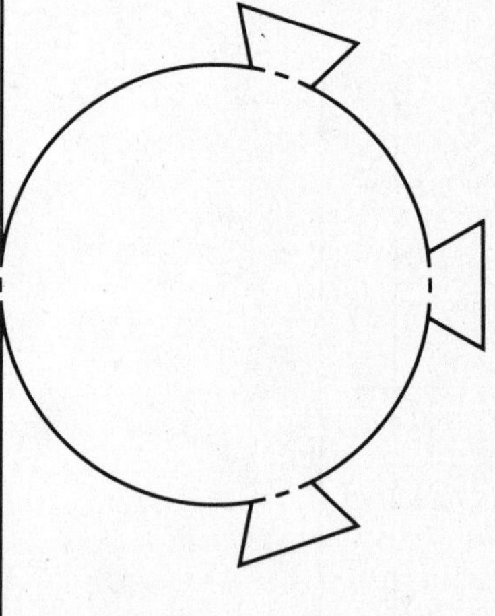

Cylinder

Name

SOLID GEOMETRIC FIGURE PATTERNS
SHEET 3

1. Cut on solid lines.
2. Fold on dashed lines.
3. Tape or glue to form solid shapes.

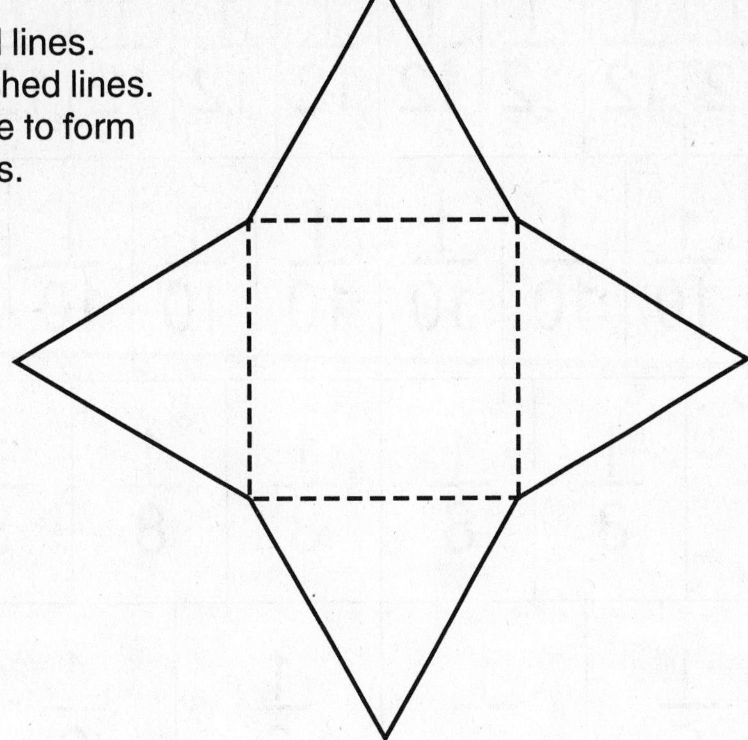

Square Pyramid

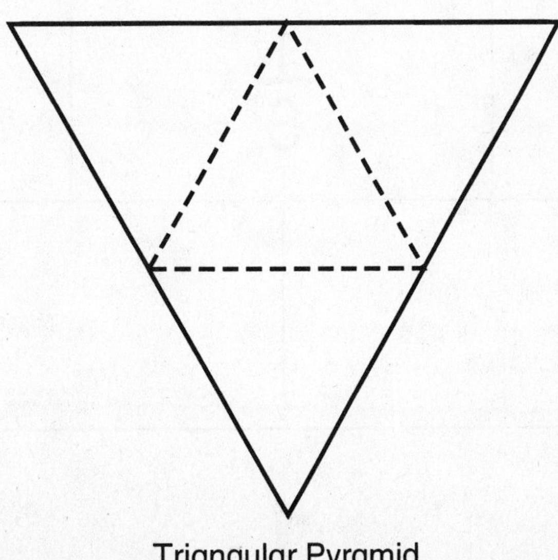

Triangular Pyramid

Name ______________________________

FRACTION STRIPS

$\frac{1}{12}$	$\frac{1}{12}$	$\frac{1}{12}$	$\frac{1}{12}$	$\frac{1}{12}$	$\frac{1}{12}$	$\frac{1}{12}$	$\frac{1}{12}$	$\frac{1}{12}$	$\frac{1}{12}$	$\frac{1}{12}$	$\frac{1}{12}$

$\frac{1}{10}$	$\frac{1}{10}$	$\frac{1}{10}$	$\frac{1}{10}$	$\frac{1}{10}$	$\frac{1}{10}$	$\frac{1}{10}$	$\frac{1}{10}$	$\frac{1}{10}$	$\frac{1}{10}$

$\frac{1}{8}$	$\frac{1}{8}$	$\frac{1}{8}$	$\frac{1}{8}$	$\frac{1}{8}$	$\frac{1}{8}$	$\frac{1}{8}$	$\frac{1}{8}$

$\frac{1}{6}$	$\frac{1}{6}$	$\frac{1}{6}$	$\frac{1}{6}$	$\frac{1}{6}$	$\frac{1}{6}$

$\frac{1}{4}$	$\frac{1}{4}$	$\frac{1}{4}$	$\frac{1}{4}$

$\frac{1}{3}$	$\frac{1}{3}$	$\frac{1}{3}$

$\frac{1}{2}$	$\frac{1}{2}$

1

Name

FRACTION CIRCLES

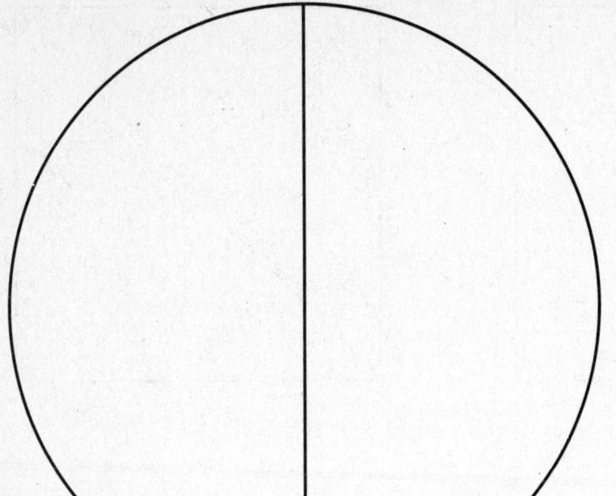

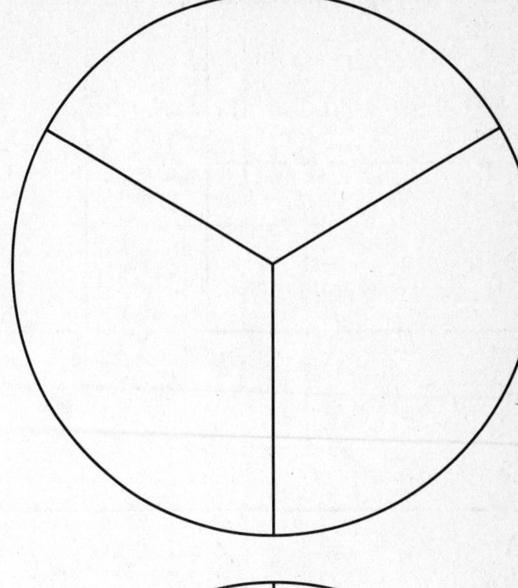

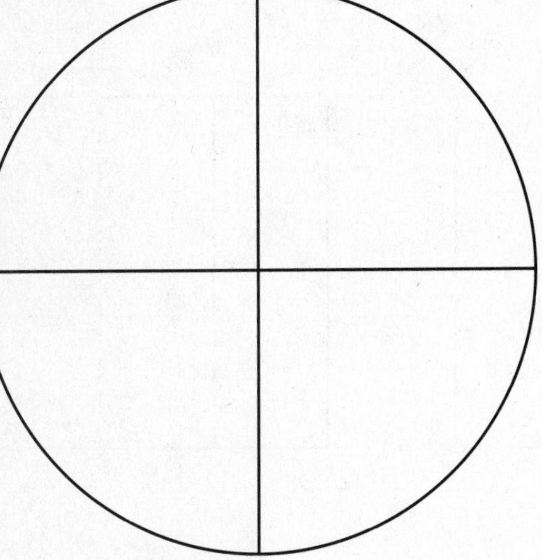

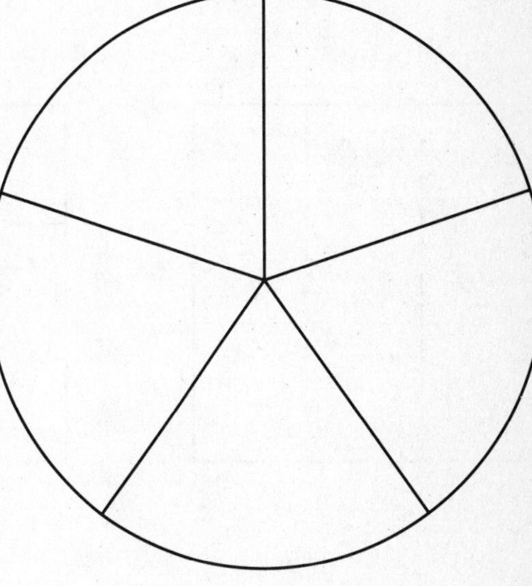

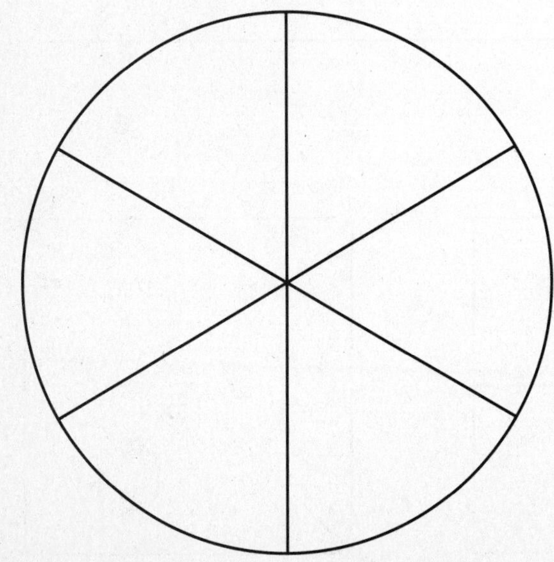

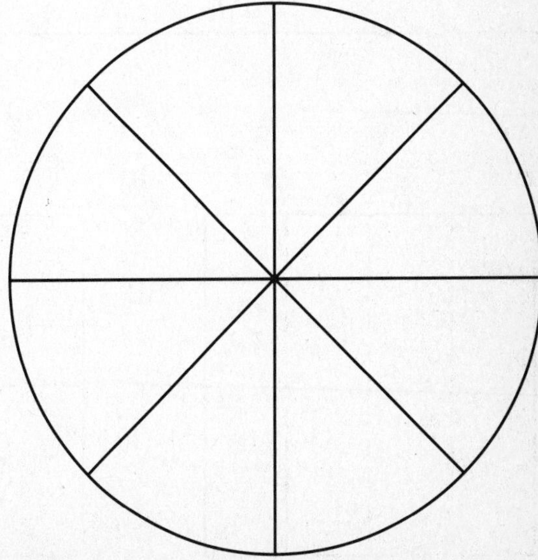

Name

FRACTION SQUARES

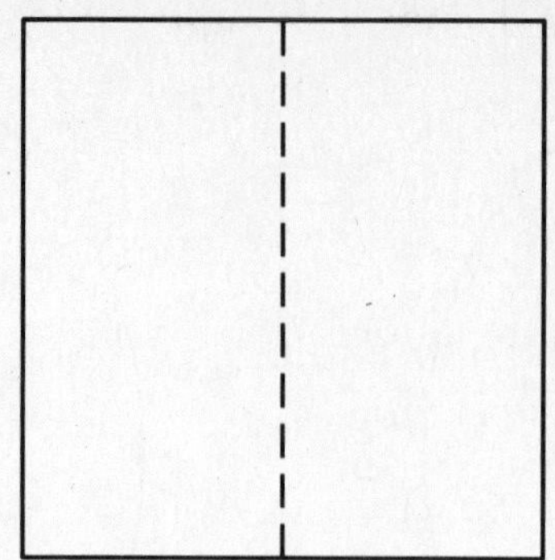
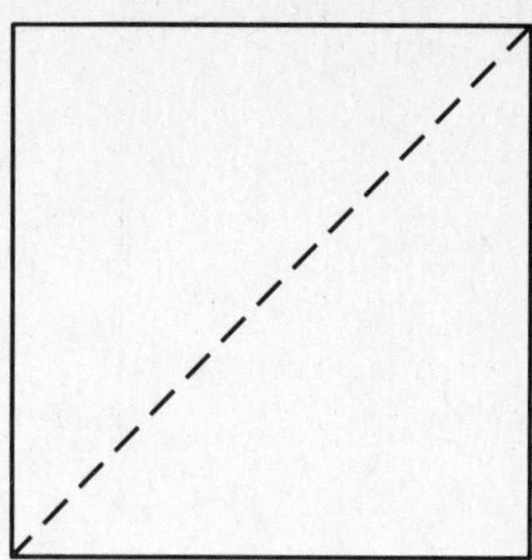

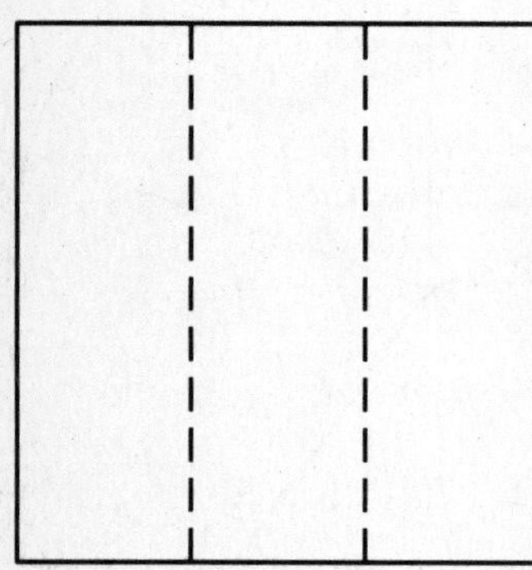
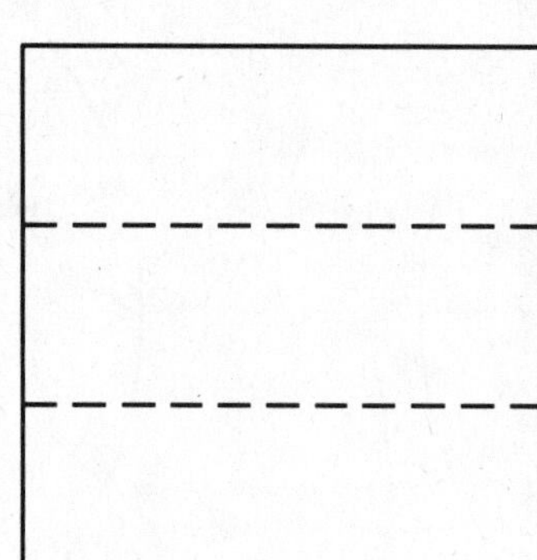
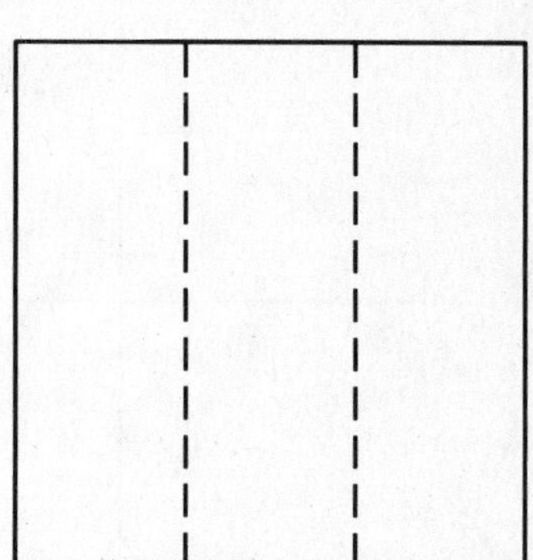

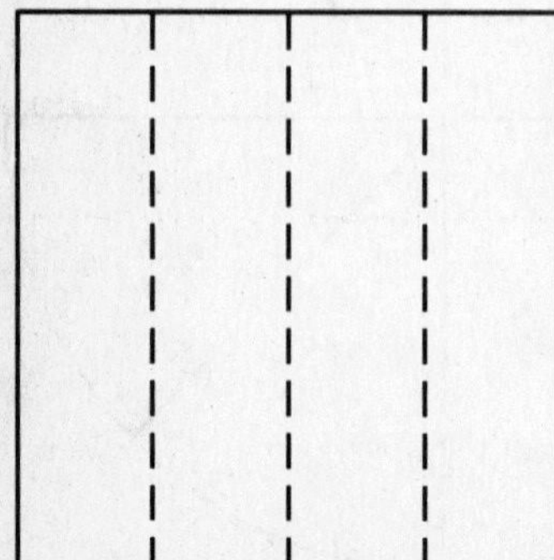
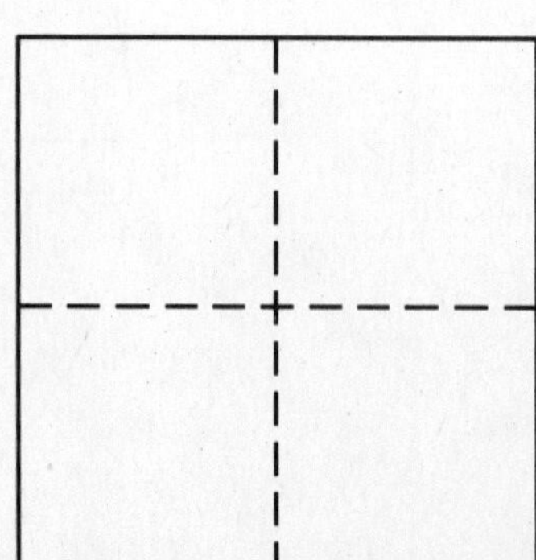
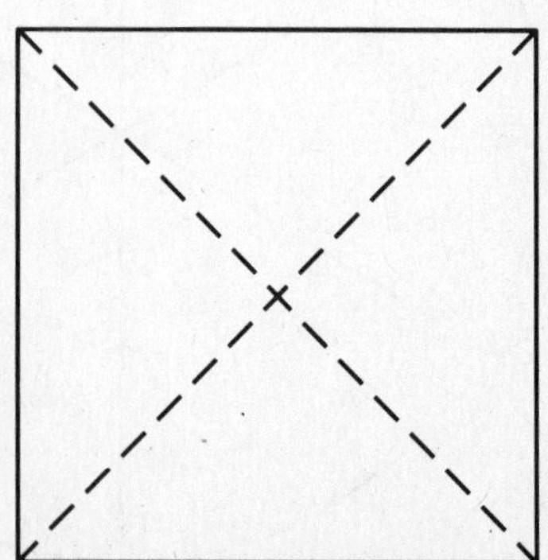

Name

NUMBER CARDS

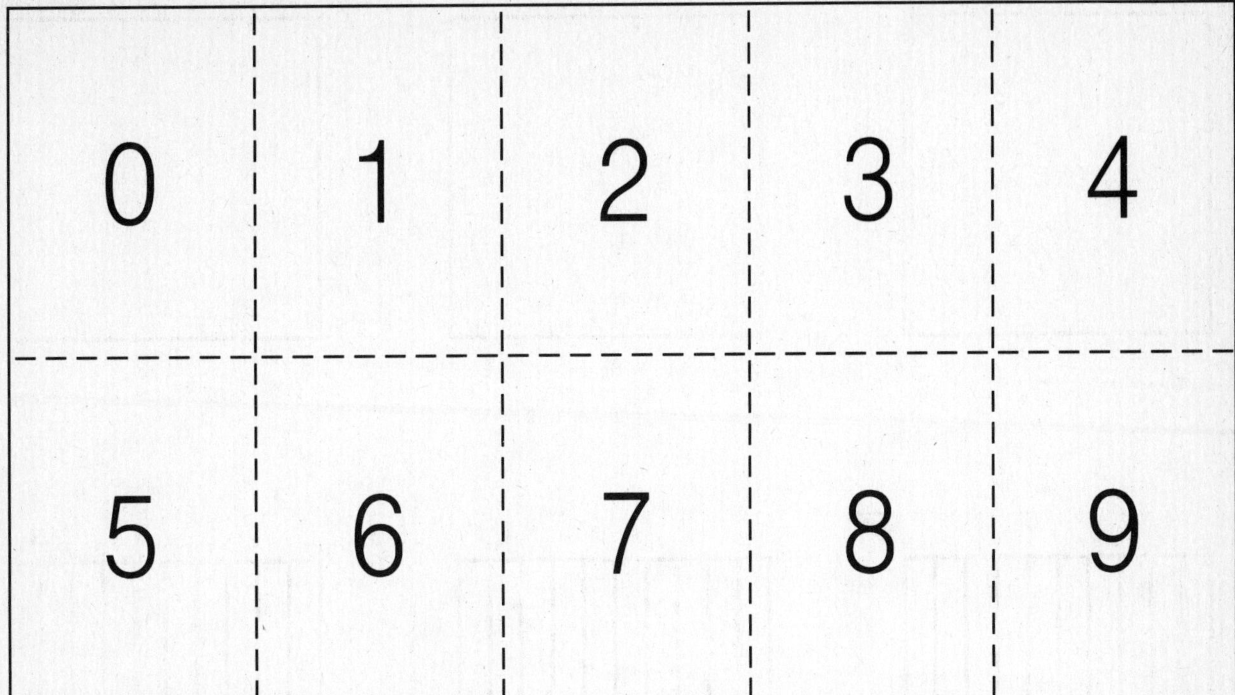

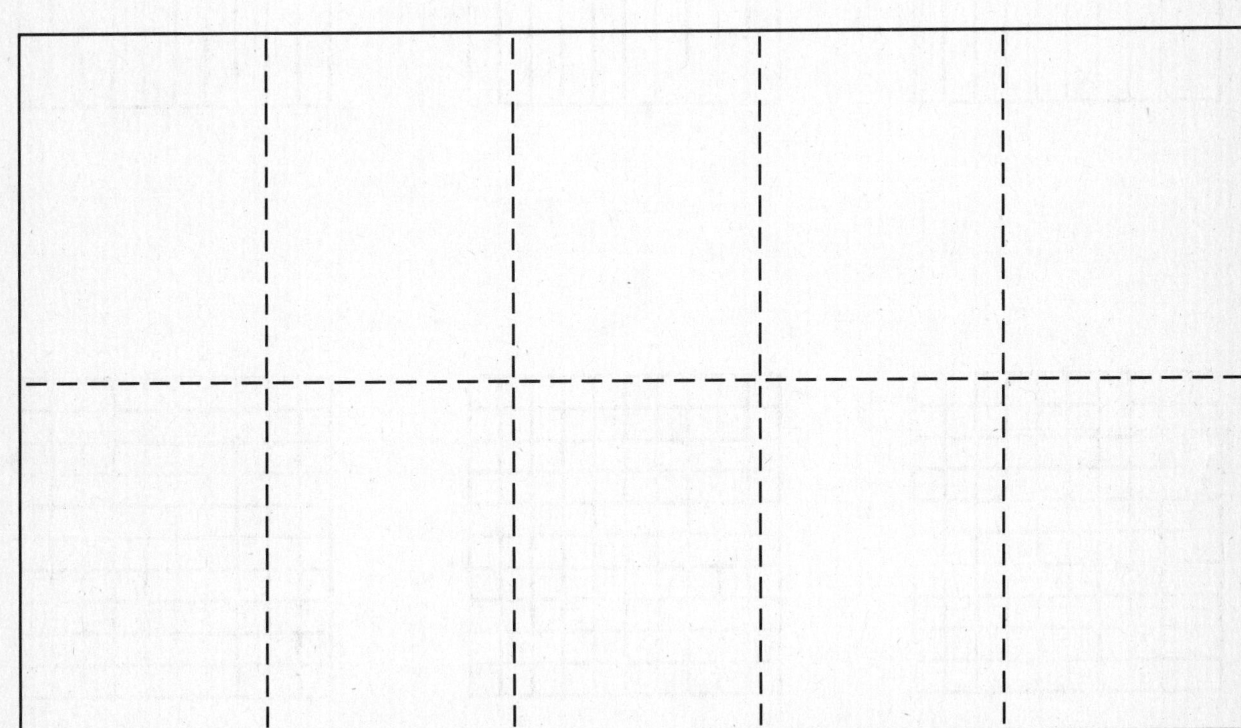

Name

DECIMAL SQUARES

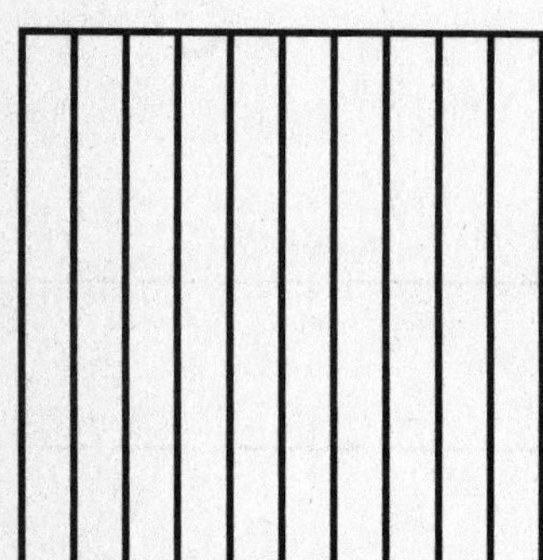
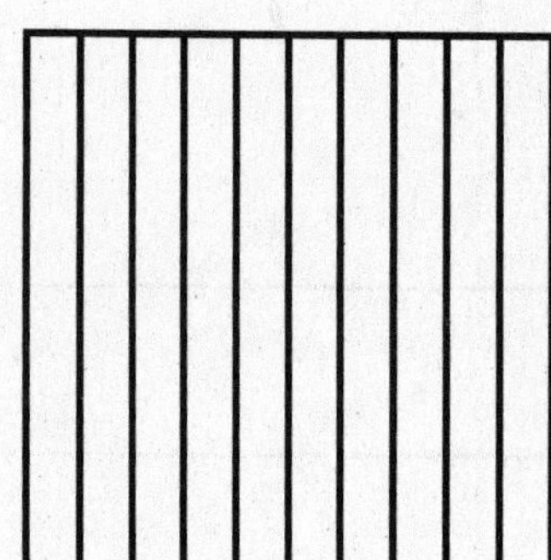
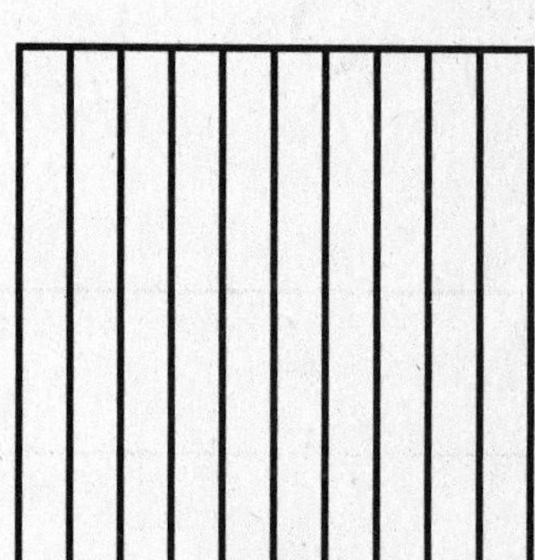

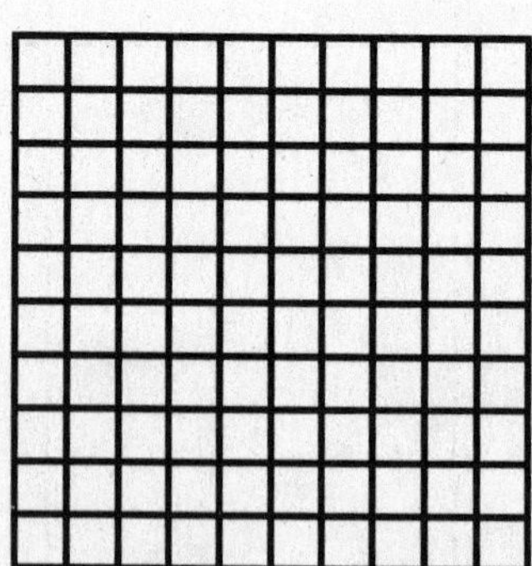
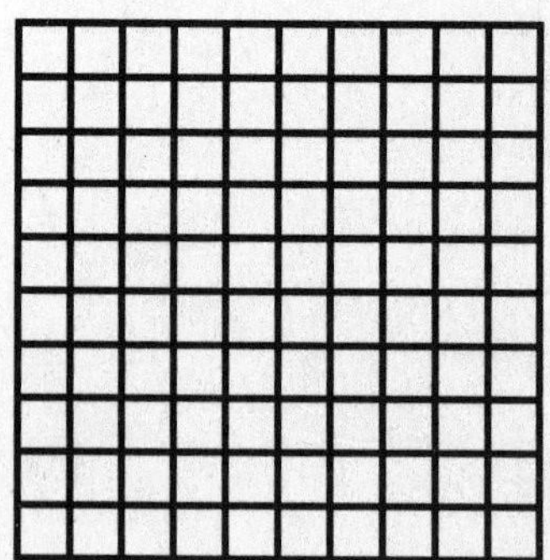

Name

MATH CENTER RECORDING SHEET

Practice Activity ___
Problem-Solving Activity ___

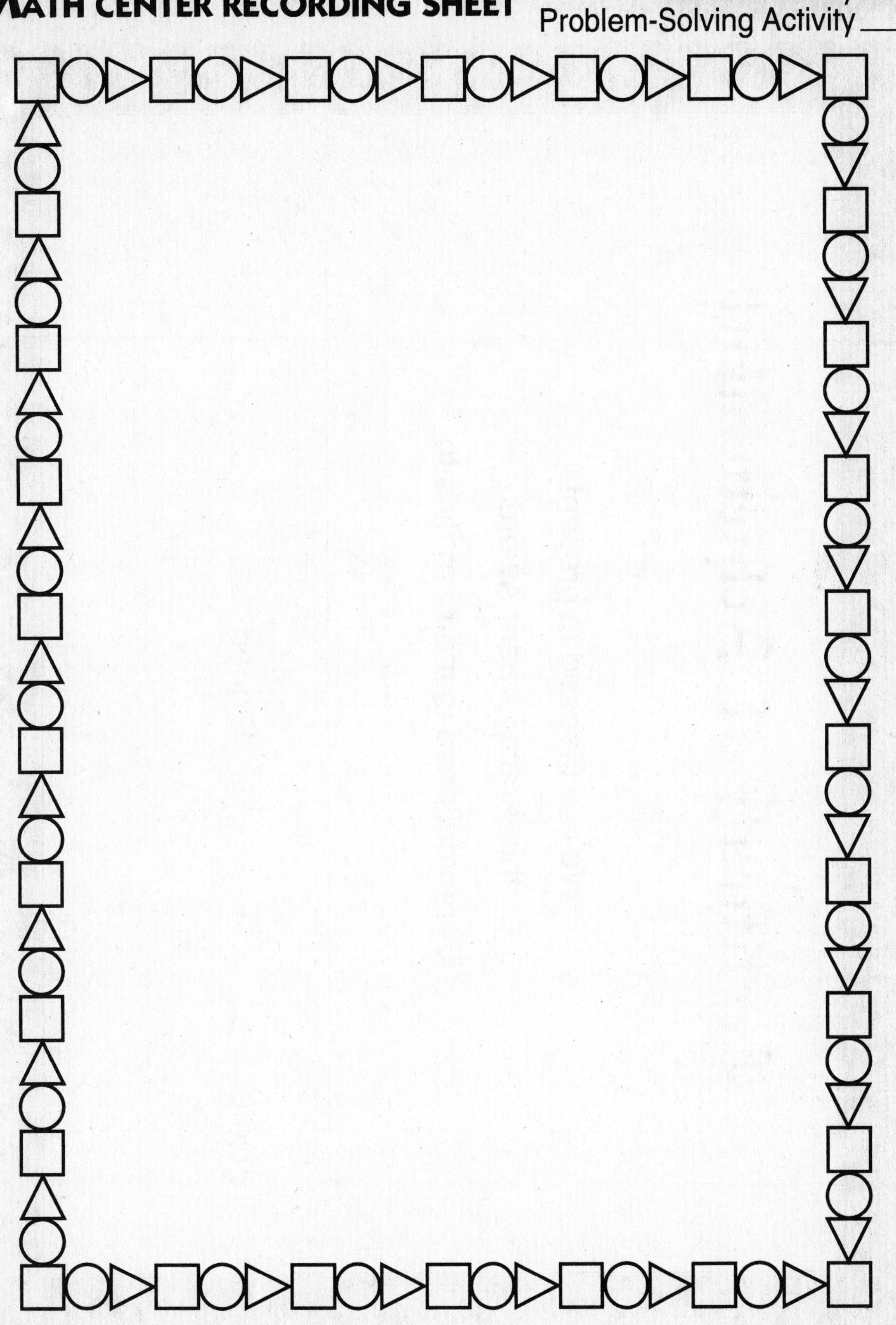

Name ______________________________

ACHIEVEMENT AWARD

Certificate of Achievement

We are pleased to present
this Achievement Award
for excellence in mathematics to

____

Date ____________ Signed ______________________________

____